A Literature Kit™ FOR

Because of Winn-Dixie

• • • • • • • • • • • • • • • • • • •

By Kate DiCamillo

Written by David McAleese

GRADES 3 - 4

Classroom Complete Press

P.O. Box 19729
San Diego, CA 92159
Tel: 1-800-663-3609 | Fax: 1-800-663-3608
Email: service@classroomcompletepress.com

www.classroomcompletepress.com

ISBN-13: 978-1-55319-325-8
ISBN-10: 1-55319-325-3

© 2007

Permission to Reproduce

Critical Thinking Skills

Because of Winn-Dixie

Skills For Critical Thinking		Chapter Questions										Writing Tasks	Graphic Organizers
		1-2	3-5	6-7	8-10	11	12-14	15-17	18-20	21-23	24-26		
LEVEL 1 Knowledge	• Identify Story Elements	✓		✓	✓		✓	✓	✓	✓		✓	✓
	• Recall Details	✓	✓	✓	✓	✓	✓	✓	✓		✓	✓	✓
	• Match								✓				
	• Sequence				✓						✓		
	• List					✓		✓				✓	✓
LEVEL 2 Comprehension	• Compare Characters			✓				✓	✓	✓			
	• Summarize				✓			✓				✓	
	• State Main Idea								✓				✓
	• Describe	✓								✓	✓	✓	✓
	• Interpret		✓			✓			✓	✓	✓	✓	✓
LEVEL 3 Application	• Choose Information				✓				✓			✓	✓
	• Identify Outcomes											✓	
	• Apply What Is Learned						✓		✓				
	• Make Connections		✓		✓	✓	✓	✓	✓				✓
LEVEL 4 Analysis	• Draw Conclusions	✓		✓		✓		✓	✓	✓	✓	✓	✓
	• Identify Supporting Evidence				✓	✓	✓	✓	✓	✓	✓	✓	✓
	• Infer Character Motivations	✓	✓		✓	✓				✓	✓	✓	✓
	• Identify Cause & Effect				✓					✓	✓	✓	
	• Identify Relationships				✓	✓	✓	✓		✓	✓		✓
LEVEL 5 Synthesis	• Predict								✓	✓	✓		
	• Design (i.e., An Invitation)											✓	
	• Create				✓							✓	✓
	• Imagine Alternatives			✓								✓	
LEVEL 6 Evaluation	• State & Defend An Opinion	✓	✓	✓		✓	✓	✓	✓	✓	✓	✓	✓
	• Make Judgements				✓		✓	✓		✓	✓	✓	✓
	• Explain				✓	✓				✓	✓	✓	✓

Based on Bloom's Taxonomy

Contents

● ● ● ● ● ● ● ● ● ● ● ● ● ● ● ●

FREE!

✔ **6 BONUS** Activity Pages! **Additional worksheets for your students**
✔ **3 BONUS** Overhead Transparencies! **For use with your projection system**
- Go to our website: **www.classroomcompletepress.com/bonus**
- Enter item CC2301 or Because of Winn-Dixie
- Enter pass code CC2301D for Activity Pages. CC2301A for Overheads.

Assessment Rubric

Because of Winn-Dixie

Student's Name: _____

Assignment: _____

Level: _____

	Level 1	Level 2	Level 3	Level 4
Comprehension of the Novel	Demonstrates a limited understanding of the novel. Requires teacher intervention	Demonstrates a basic understanding of the novel's content	Demonstrates a good understanding of the novel's content	Demonstrates a thorough understanding of the novel's content
Response to the Text	Expresses responses to the text with limited effectiveness, inconsistently supported by proof from the text	Expresses responses to the text with some effectiveness, supported with some proof from the text	Expresses responses to the text with appropriate skills, supported with appropriate proof from the text	Expresses thorough and complete responses to the text, supported by concise and effective proof from the text
Interpretation and Analysis	Interprets and explains various elements of the text with few, unrelated details and incorrect analysis	Interprets and explains various elements of the text with some detail, but with some inconsistent analysis	Interprets and explains various elements of the text with appropriate detail and analysis	Effectively interprets and explains various elements of the text with consistent, clear and effective detail and analysis

STRENGTHS:

WEAKNESSES:

NEXT STEPS:

© CLASSROOM COMPLETE PRESS

4

Because of Winn-Dixie CC2301

Teacher Guide

This resource has been created for ease of use by both TEACHERS and STUDENTS alike.

Introduction

Since she published her first novel, **Because of Winn-Dixie**, which was recognized as a Newbery Medal Honor Book, Kate DiCamillo has been sharing her fine writing style and sensitive stories with us all. Her novels deal frequently with the themes of loss, longing, love, and the importance of finding a place where one belongs and finds contentment. This contentment, such as Opal finds at the end of **Because of Winn-Dixie**, frees Kate DiCamillo's characters to come to terms with their losses, longings, and sadness, and allows them to eventually move on.

How Is This Literature Kit™ Organized?
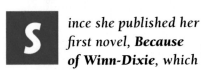

STUDENT HANDOUTS

Chapter Activities (in the form of reproducible worksheets) make up the majority of this resource. For each chapter or group of chapters there are BEFORE YOU READ activities and AFTER YOU READ activities.

• The BEFORE YOU READ activities prepare students for reading by setting a purpose for reading. They stimulate background knowledge and experience, and guide students to make connections between what they know and what they will learn. Important concepts and vocabulary from the chapter(s) are also presented.

• The AFTER YOU READ activities check students' comprehension and extend their learning. Students are asked to give thoughtful consideration of the text through creative and evaluative short-answer questions and journal prompts.

Six **Writing Tasks** and three **Graphic Organizers** are included to further develop students' critical thinking and writing skills, and analysis of the text. (See page 6 for suggestions on using the Graphic Organizers.) The **Assessment Rubric** (page 4) is a useful tool for evaluating students' responses to the Writing Tasks and Graphic Organizers.

PICTURE CUES

This resource contains three main types of pages, each with a different purpose and use. A **Picture Cue** at the top of each page shows, at a glance, what the page is for.

 Teacher Guide
• Information and tools for the teacher

 Student Handout
• Reproducible worksheets and activities

 Easy Marking™ Answer Key
• Answers for student activities

EASY MARKING™ ANSWER KEY
Marking students' worksheets is fast and easy with this **Answer Key**. Answers are listed in columns – just line up the column with its corresponding worksheet, as shown, and see how every question matches up with its answer!

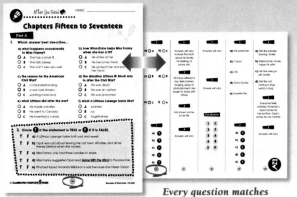

Every question matches up with its answer!

1,2,3
Graphic Organizer Transparencies

The three **Graphic Organizer Transparencies** included in this Literature Kit™ are especially suited to a study of *Because of Winn-Dixie*. Below are suggestions for using each organizer in your classroom, or they may be adapted to suit the individual needs of your students. The transparencies can be used on an overhead projector in teacher-led activities, and/or photocopied for use as student worksheets. To evaluate students' responses to any of the organizers, you may wish to use the **Assessment Rubric** (*on page 4*).

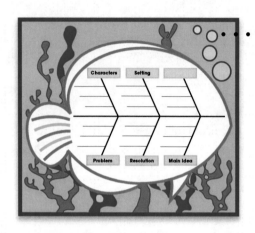

FISHBONE GRAPHIC ORGANIZER

A Fishbone Graphic Organizer is an effective tool for collecting and recording information as students read through the novel. Use each "bone" to jot down point form notes, phrases, or ideas about different aspects of the novel. For instance, the setting "bone" is a place to record words that describe the time and place, and possibly atmosphere of the novel. The Fishbone is also an excellent springboard for further discussion and writing. Completed, it can be used as an overview of the novel, or as rough notes for more detailed responses, such as in a book report. It is important to review each of the story elements on the Fishbone before reading. Students can add extra lines to each bone if more room is required. **Found on Page 53.**

PERSONAL RESPONSE: WRITING OPINIONS, MAKING CONNECTIONS

With this Personal Response Organizer students discuss and evaluate what they have read. It focuses students' attention on making connections between the text and their own ideas, feelings, and experiences (*i.e., life experiences and experiences with text and other forms of communication*). Students express their opinions of the book and provide supporting evidence from the text, ask any questions they still have as a prompt for further discussion, and visualize a scene from the novel. As a beginning point for this activity, explain the expectation that as they write their answers, students must always support their opinions, etc., with examples from the text. **Found on Page 54.**

TREE GRAPHIC ORGANIZER

Like Gloria Dump's ghost tree in shape, this organizer allows students to examine various aspects of the novel. If Opal's name is written on the sign on the trunk, and the names of five other characters are written in the ovals, with one name per oval, the rectangular boxes can serve as a place to describe the relationship Opal has with each character. Similarly, with Opal's name on the tree trunk sign, students can write one of the novel's themes in each oval (*i.e., loss, loneliness, abandonment, loving those around you, etc.*), and in the rectangular boxes explain how each relates to Opal's life. **Found on Page 55.**

Bloom's Taxonomy* for Reading Comprehension

The activities in this resource engage and build the full range of thinking skills that are essential for students' reading comprehension. Based on the six levels of thinking in Bloom's Taxonomy, questions are given that challenge students to not only recall what they have read, but move beyond this to understand the text through higher-order thinking. By using higher-order skills of applying, analysing, evaluating and creating, students become active readers, drawing more meaning from the text, and applying and extending their learning in more sophisticated ways.

This **Literature Kit**™, therefore, is an effective tool for any Language Arts program. Whether it is used in whole or in part, or adapted to meet individual student needs, this resource provides teachers with the important questions to ask, inspiring students' interest, creativity, and promoting meaningful learning.

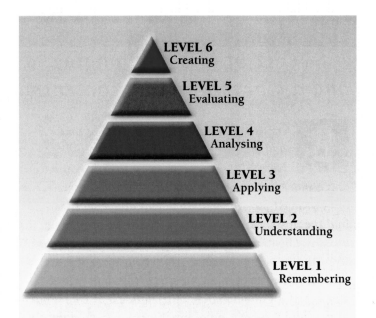

**BLOOM'S TAXONOMY:
6 LEVELS OF THINKING**

Bloom's Taxonomy is a widely used tool by educators for classifying learning objectives, and is based on the work of Benjamin Bloom.

Teaching Strategies — WHOLE-CLASS, SMALL GROUP AND INDEPENDENT STUDY

Because of Winn-Dixie is a novel that may be approached in several ways. Most obvious is as a traditional, whole-class read-aloud, perhaps applying some shared or modeled reading, focusing on the author's skills, choices made in writing, and the elements of the narrative. The BEFORE YOU READ and AFTER YOU READ activities in this **Literature Kit**™ provide a basis for such discussions. To facilitate independent study learning, these activities have been divided into chapter groupings to allow students to work on manageable sections of the novel, and not feel overwhelmed by the activities.

Another approach is to use this book as a springboard for small group activities that focus on a variety of aspects of the novel. For example, while there are several tense scenes of

confusion and action, as in the scenes when the thunderstorms strike, elsewhere it is the portrayal of each character, Opal's delicately developing friendships, and the conversations had by the characters, that come to dominate the text. An effective strategy to use if choosing this approach is a jigsaw strategy. Divide your class into four or five heterogeneous groups, assigning one member of each group to a character. Have these groups break into expert groups, each of which will only focus on a single character, as they collect information about that character. When finished, have the students return to their original group, and share what they have learned. All members of your class will be engaged in this approach, and will use reading, writing, and oral language skills in the process.

Summary of the Story

A STORY of loss and longing, a story of loneliness and friendships, and a story of finding contentment and a place for oneself.

Because of Winn-Dixie is a story of loss and longing, a story of loneliness and friendships, and a story of finding contentment and a place for oneself. It is a story in which a ten-year-old girl must face the abandonment of her mother, and find the answer to the question "Will she ever come back?". The answer, surprisingly, is "No!", but India Opal Buloni, over the course of the novel, learns to deal with this answer through her experiences and support of a growing circle of friends, all of whom have also suffered some kind of loss themselves. And finally, it is the story of the love between a girl and her dog, a pet who has an uncanny ability to bring kindred spirits together.

Opal first finds Winn-Dixie as a stray, running through the local Winn-Dixie grocery store. When the store workers call for the dog to be caught and sent to the pound, Opal claims the stray is her pet, names him Winn-Dixie on the spot, and takes him home. Instantly, Opal feels some importance, as she now has a "less fortunate" in her care. Even her father, whom she calls the preacher because he spends so much time at that job, agrees to keep the dog. Soon, Winn-Dixie has the preacher lowering his guard, and he tells Opal, for the first time, ten things about her mother who had run away years before the novel takes place.

With Winn-Dixie at her side, Opal begins to explore her new town of Naomi, Florida. She meets Miss Franny Block, the librarian who loves to tell stories, and whose friends are long dead. Then there's Gloria Dump, the near-blind old woman who some think is a witch, but who really is a true friend with years of experience to back up her sage advice. Otis, and ex-convict, works in the local pet store, and has a magical ability to calm animals with his guitar playing. Rounding out Opal's growing list of friends are pinch-faced Amanda Wilkinson, mourning the death of her young brother, Sweetie Pie Thomas, a five-year-old who loves dogs and parties with a theme, and the two bald-headed babies, Stevie and Dunlap Dewberry.

The characters are eventually brought together for a garden party. At the climax of the novel, when Opal thinks that Winn-Dixie has run off in a thunderstorm, she confronts her father about her mother's departure. Realizing that she will probably never come back, Opal gains a deeper appreciation of her new friends. In the end she joins them as they sing, paying close attention to remember them all and their song.

Suggestions for Further Reading

BOOKS BY KATE DICAMILLO

The Tiger Rising © 2002
The Tale of Despereaux © 2003
Mercy Watson to the Rescue © 2005
Mercy Watson Goes for a Ride © 2006
The Miraculous Journey of Edward Tulane © 2006

OTHER RECOMMENDED RESOURCES
Fred Gipson, *Old Yeller* ©1956
William H. Armstrong, *Sounder* ©1969
Sharon Creech, *Love That Dog* © 2001
Wilson Rawls, *Where the Red Fern Grows* © 1961

Vocabulary

CHAPTERS 1 AND 2
• preacher • distracted • hollered • matted-up • macaroni • manager • vegetables • ugly • wagged • produce • concerned • everybody • trotting • department • missionary • employee • India • suffering • exception • manners • fortunate

CHAPTERS 3 TO 5
• shiny • handsome • ten • funny • soft • orphans • wiggled • straight • situation • relieved • understand • finally • hoping • toothbrush • trailer • agreed • freckles • ceiling • microscope • softly • memorized • howling • empty • barbecue • church

CHAPTERS 6 AND 7
• librarian • bear • friend • ma'am • mosquitoes • library • reader • stories • mood • woman • window • humming • scary • positive • trembling • shaking • weight • experience • properly • snuffled • palmetto • appear • peculiar • recalls • comfort

CHAPTERS 8 TO 10
• gerbil • furious • installment • trustworthy • overgrown • crinkly • supplies • expensive • leash • furious • situation • irritating • collar • parrot • swept • separated • knuckle • introduced • jungle • general • whiskers • yawning • snoring

CHAPTER 11
• whining • whimpering • trembling • shaking • flew • panting • screamed • loved • thunderstorm • lightning • knelt • wild • barreling • pathological • reasoned • normal • poked • sentence • terrorized • surely • crept • intend • forgive

CHAPTERS 12 TO 14
• shouted • told • asked • holler • whispered • prettiest • lizard • guitar • dreamy • croaked • slithering • through • counter • shelves • hugged • arranging • straight • ignorant • stories • criminal • bottles • growled • studied

CHAPTERS 15 TO 17
• air conditioning • novel • lozenge • sorrow • around • comfort • dandelion • protecting • fit • fortune • ghosts • chattering • wonderful • slavery • money • manufactured • shrugged • dramatic • slamming • cuss • battlefield

CHAPTERS 18 TO 20
• sorrowful • melancholy • idle • conversation • theme • surprises • candies • unwrapped • peculiar • wrappers • built • apologize • drowned • suffering • tragedies • tongue • stomach • listened • great-grandfather • hunching • sniffed

CHAPTERS 21 TO 23
• convinced • wagging • desperately • smiling • somebody • flashlight • downpour • grapefruit • convinced • cooler • frilly • famous • decorate • swollen • shimmery • wobble • magazines • serious • nervous • pickles • introduced • amuse • pleasure • appreciate • platter • teetery • protecting • underneath • umbrellas • porch

CHAPTERS 24 TO 26
• downtown • taillight • memorize • drizzle • realize • railroad • neighborhood • snored • upset • question • tighter • whistling • cane • plumb • squawked • disappointed • toads • burglar • breeze • constellations • planets • branches • praying • million • leaning • cracked • echoed • strummed

Kate DiCamillo

Kate DiCamillo writes in an easy-to-read manner, using carefully chosen words to create realistic characters and settings.

Since she published her first novel, **Because of Winn-Dixie**, Kate DiCamillo has been sharing her fine writing style and sensitive stories with us all. **Because of Winn-Dixie** was recognized as a Newbery Medal Honor Book, and **The Tale of Despereaux** won the Newbery Medal, as the best children's book of 2004!

Kate DiCamillo has introduced us to a wonderful world of characters with whom we can all make connections. The characters in her novels all deal with similar feelings. The themes of abandonment, sadness, longing, and eventual love for the things around us, bring her characters to life with a richness that makes them seem so believable to us. In **Because of Winn-Dixie**, India Opal Buloni searches for the reason why her mother left she and her father. She longs for an answer, but instead is faced with her father's silence on the matter. It is only after she rescues Winn-Dixie from the grocery store that events begin to unfold that show her that it is all right to remember things that have passed, but that it is more important to love those around you in the present, and to move on. Strangely, it is through her developing relationship with Winn-Dixie that she opens up to her father, and he to her. And it is through Winn-Dixie, whether he is running through a grocery store, entering a library or a pet store, or bringing India Opal and others, all of whom have some sense of being left out or abandoned, together as friends, that India Opal at last finds contentment and a place where she truly feels she belongs.

Kate DiCamillo writes in an easy-to-read manner, using carefully chosen words to create realistic characters and settings. Her books are easy to enjoy, because we each can find a little bit of ourselves in the actions, situations, thoughts, and feelings that her characters experience.

Did You Know?
- **Kate DiCamillo grew up in Florida, the setting of Because of Winn-Dixie!**
- **Winn-Dixie is a real grocery store!**
- **Because of Winn-Dixie has been made into a movie!**

Chapters One and Two

Answer the questions in complete sentences.

1. Before you begin the novel, look at the cover of the book. What does it show? What does it suggest to you that the book might be about? Explain.

_____

_____

2. If you could have any pet you like, what kind of animal would it be? Why would you choose that animal? How do you think your parents might react to your choice?

_____

_____

Vocabulary

The author, Kate DiCamillo, uses carefully chosen words to help create realistic characters in this novel. Read each quote from the story and, using context clues, write what you think the underlined words mean. Then, check your ideas using a dictionary.

1. I also told him about the **_preacher_** and how he was a good man, even if he was too **_distracted_** with sermons and prayers and suffering people to go grocery shopping.

a) In this sentence, **preacher** means _____

b) In this sentence, **distracted** means _____

2. I went to the trailer door and I **_hollered_**, "Winn-Dixie!"

In this sentence, **hollered** means _____

3. He looked at his ribs and his **_matted_**-up fur and the places where he was bald.

In this sentence, **matted** means _____

Chapters One and Two

Part A

1. Which answer best describes...

a) Winn-Dixie?

○ **A**   a clean dog
○ **B**   a stray dog
○ **C**   a small dog

c) Opal?

○ **A**   a good artist
○ **B**   tall and fast
○ **C**   good and quiet

e) the time in which the story takes place?

○ **A**   autumn
○ **B**   summertime
○ **C**   winter

b) Opal's reaction to Winn-Dixie's "smile" and sense of humor?

○ **A**   She laughed out loud.
○ **B**   She was startled.
○ **C**   She fell in love with him.

d) the preacher?

○ **A**   a turtle in its shell
○ **B**   a sleepy dog
○ **C**   a wise owl

f) the Friendly Corners Trailer Park?

○ **A**   for families
○ **B**   a truck stop
○ **C**   for adults only

2. Circle T if the statement is TRUE or F if it is FALSE.

T   F   **a)** In the grocery store, when Opal first called the stray dog Winn-Dixie, the dog trotted over to see her as if it was his name.

T   F   **b)** Winn-Dixie was a healthy looking dog, with thick, shiny brown fur.

T   F   **c)** Opal calls her dad "the preacher" instead of Dad.

T   F   **d)** The setting of the novel is a town called Naomi, Florida.

T   F   **e)** The preacher always told Opal to help those less fortunate than herself.

Chapters One and Two

Part B

Answer the questions in complete sentences.

1. Why did Opal decide to help the stray dog in the Winn-Dixie grocery store? Do you think she did the right thing? Explain your opinion.

_____

_____

2. What can we infer about Opal from her decision to help Winn-Dixie?

_____

_____

3. Using facts from the first two chapters, how would you describe Opal's daily life? Think about where she lives and the kinds of things she does.

_____

_____

4. What can you infer from Opal's description of her father as being like "**a turtle hiding inside its shell**"? What does it tell us about his personality?

_____

_____

5. How would you describe Winn-Dixie's affect on the preacher? Consider what we learn about his job and his personality in these first two chapters.

_____

_____

Journal Activity

India Opal Buloni is the narrator of the novel, and we see everything from her point of view. If you were in her place, how would you have reacted to Winn-Dixie? Would you have fallen in love with him as easily?

Chapters Three to Five

Answer the questions in complete sentences.

1. Before you begin the next few chapters, think about Winn-Dixie. What did Opal and her father mean when they said he was a **"Less Fortunate"**? Explain in your own words.

   _____

   _____

2. Think about someone in your family, maybe your mom or dad, maybe a brother or a sister, or maybe another relative. Write down five things that make that family member special to you.

   _____

   _____

Vocabulary

ADJECTIVES are words that describe nouns. Kate DiCamillo uses carefully chosen adjectives in <u>Because of Winn-Dixie</u> to put clear pictures in our minds of the characters and the various settings. Below are some adjectives from chapters three to five. Place them in the boxes so that the sentences become more descriptive.

shiny   handsome   ten   funny   soft

1. After Winn-Dixie was cleaned, he was very [   ] .

2. Opal learned [   ] things about her mother.

3. Winn-Dixie's fur was [   ] and [   ] .

4. Winn-Dixie always smiles in a [   ] way.

After You Read 📖

Chapters Three to Five

Part A

Put a check mark next to the answer that is most correct.

1. **Why does Opal decide to ask the preacher to tell her about her mother?**

○ **A**   She wants to bring him out of his turtle's shell.

○ **B**   After having a "conversation" with Winn-Dixie, she finally has the courage to ask him after Winn-Dixie "encourages" her with twitching ears, raised eyebrows, stares, and a sneeze.

○ **C**   Opal has not made any friends since moving to Naomi.

2. **When Opal asks the preacher to tell her about her mother, she asks him to tell her ten things. Why does she ask for ten things?**

○ **A**   She wants one thing for each year of her life.

○ **B**   Ten is a nice, round number.

○ **C**   Winn-Dixie barked ten times.

3. **Just before the preacher tells Opal the ten things about her mother, he looks at Winn-Dixie and says, *"I should have guessed you were going to be trouble."* What does he mean by this?**

○ **A**   Winn-Dixie has made a mess inside their trailer, and it will take several days to clean.

○ **B**   Winn-Dixie requires a great deal of effort to keep clean and fed, and the preacher isn't sure they can afford it.

○ **C**   By being a friend to Opal, and encouraging her to ask about her mother, and by nudging the preacher to begin speaking, Winn-Dixie has made them both do something they had not done before.

4. **Why did Winn-Dixie pull the cushions down, pull all the toilet paper off the roll, and howl until Mrs. Detweller's dog howled too?**

○ **A**   Winn-Dixie is a mischievous dog.

○ **B**   Winn-Dixie did not like to be left alone.

○ **C**   Winn-Dixie did not like the trailer park.

Chapters Three to Five

Part B

Answer the questions in complete sentences.

1. How would you explain Winn-Dixie's reactions to Opal's story and questions about her mother? Was he really encouraging her to speak to the preacher? Explain your opinion.

    _____

    _____

2. What can we infer about the preacher's first reaction to Opal's request to know ten things about her mother? Opal says that he "**held real still. I could see him thinking about pulling his head back into his shell.**" Give two reasons for your answer.

    _____

    _____

3. Why does Opal write down the ten things her father told her about her mother?

    _____

    _____

4. Why does Opal tell God that she is lonely in Naomi, even with Winn-Dixie as a pet?

    _____

    _____

Journal Activity

Have you ever looked at an animal, perhaps an endangered animal, or perhaps even a pet of your own, and wondered what it would say to you if it could talk? If you could talk to that animal, what would you ask it? How do you think it would answer?

NAME: _____

Chapters Six and Seven

Answer the questions in complete sentences.

1. What kind of books do you like to take out of the library?

_____

2. If you could have a library of your own, and you could arrange it in any way that you like, with the books that you enjoy, what would it be like? Tell three things about your special library. (You might even want to design it on another piece of paper!)

_____

_____

Vocabulary

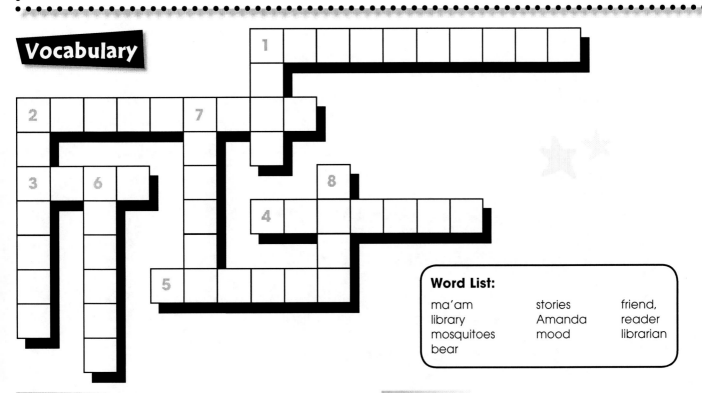

Word List:

ma'am	stories	friend,
library	Amanda	reader
mosquitoes	mood	librarian
bear		

Across

1. biting insects
2. a person who works in a library
3. a furry animal
4. fiction books
5. a person who you play with

Down

1. a short way of saying "madam"
2. a building where there are many books
6. a pinch-faced girl
7. a person who reads
8. the way you feel

Chapters Six and Seven

Part A

1. **Which answer best describes...**

a) Miss Franny Block?
- ○ **A** someone who misses her friends
- ○ **B** mean and old
- ○ **C** tall and fair

c) the animal that once went into Miss Franny's library?
- ○ **A** a fox
- ○ **B** a bear
- ○ **C** a badger

e) how the men in town treated Miss Franny?
- ○ **A** teased her
- ○ **B** laughed at her
- ○ **C** pointed at her

b) the reason why Miss Franny was given a library?
- ○ **A** a wedding present
- ○ **B** a treat
- ○ **C** a birthday present

d) how Miss Franny scared the bear away?
- ○ **A** whistled at it
- ○ **B** turned the light on and off
- ○ **C** threw a book and yelled at it

f) how Winn-Dixie reacted to the story?
- ○ **A** he barked
- ○ **B** he smiled
- ○ **C** he wagged his tail

2. **Circle** **T** if the statement is TRUE or **F** if it is FALSE.

T F **a)** Miss Franny, a small old woman who runs the library in Naomi, was the first friend Opal made there.

T F **b)** Miss Franny thought Winn-Dixie was a bear.

T F **c)** Dogs are allowed in the Herman W. Block Memorial Library.

T F **d)** Miss Franny threw the novel <u>War and Peace</u> at the bear.

T F **e)** Pinched-faced Amanda Wilkinson is friendly to Opal.

Chapters Six and Seven

Part B

Answer the questions in complete sentences.

1. Why did Opal spend so much time at the Herman W. Block Memorial Library that first summer in Naomi?

   _____

   _____

2. How was Miss Franny's father able to build her a library for her birthday?

   _____

   _____

3. Even though they are very different in age, Opal and Miss Franny have a lot in common. Compare two characters by listing the things they have in common.

   _____

   _____

4. What can you infer from Opal's description of Amanda Wilkinson as **"pinched-faced"**? What does Opal think of her?

   _____

   _____

5. What conclusions can you draw from Miss Franny's wink at Opal?

   _____

   _____

Journal Activity

Miss Franny sighs and seems sad when she remembers that she is alone, because her friends are all gone. Imagine if your friends all went away. How would you feel? How would your life be different?

NAME: _____

Chapters Eight to Ten

Answer the questions in complete sentences.

1. Before you begin the next few chapters, think about Opal and Winn-Dixie. Before Opal found Winn-Dixie, she was alone most of the time. Now that she has Winn-Dixie as a pet, she has discussed her mother with the preacher and she has made her first friend in Naomi. Explain, in your own words, how Winn-Dixie has helped Opal do these things.

    _____

    _____

2. Have you ever been to a pet store? Which one was it? Which part of the store is your favorite? Explain.

    _____

    _____

Vocabulary

**Using a dictionary, find the <u>meaning</u> of each of the following words.
In the boxes, write each word's <u>part of speech</u> (noun, verb, adjective, etc.).
You may illustrate your definitions if you wish.**

1. **gerbil** ☐ _____

2. **furious** ☐ _____

3. **installment** ☐ _____

4. **trustworthy** ☐ _____

5. **overgrown** ☐ _____

6. **crinkly** ☐ _____

Part A

1. **Number the events from ① to ⑤ in the order they occurred in the chapters.**

_____ **a)** Sweetie Pie Thomas laughed at the bird on Winn-Dixie's head, and then invited Opal to her birthday party with the theme of pink.

_____ **b)** Opal went to Gertrude's Pets to get Winn-Dixie a collar and a leash. At the store she met Otis, and asked to pay for Winn-Dixie's new collar and leash by working part-time at the pet store.

_____ **c)** Opal met Gloria Dump, and shared some peanut butter sandwiches with her. Gloria Dump and Opal planted a tree, and Opal began to feel much better about living in Naomi.

_____ **d)** Gertrude, the parrot, flew over and landed on top of Winn-Dixie's head, so Otis hired Opal to work in the pet store because Gertrude and Winn-Dixie get along.

_____ **e)** Dunlap and Stevie Dewberry, the brothers who looked like two bald-headed babies, warned Opal about going into the "**witch's**" garden.

2. **Which answer best describes...**

a) Gloria Dump?

○ **A** a scary witch
○ **B** an old woman without teeth
○ **C** a mean woman

b) Gloria Dump's eyesight?

○ **A** perfect vision
○ **B** like an eagle
○ **C** very poor, so that she can only see the shapes of things

c) the way in which Gloria Dump listens to Opal?

○ **A** with her heart
○ **B** attentively
○ **C** quietly

d) the reason Opal and Gloria Dump planted the tree?

○ **A** The garden was bare.
○ **B** The tree was there.
○ **C** Opal might have a green thumb like her mother.

Chapters Eight to Ten

Part B

Answer the questions in complete sentences.

1. When Opal meets Otis, he seems shy and nervous. Give two examples from the chapters that show this character trait.

    _____

    _____

2. If you were Otis, what questions would you ask Opal in an interview for the job at the pet shop? Think of the three most important.

    _____

    _____

3. Gloria Dump says that she has to rely on her heart to know people. What does she mean by this, and what does she ask Opal to do to help her get to know her?

    _____

    _____

4. When Opal gets home that night, she is very excited about her past day. Summarize everything she tells her father, and tell why it excites her.

    _____

    _____

    _____

Journal Activity

Gloria and Opal plant a tree together in the garden. It is like they are planting a new friendship together. Think about one of your best friends. What have you done together to help your friendship grow?

Chapter Eleven

Answer the questions in complete sentences.

1. At the beginning of Chapter Nine, Opal says, "**Just about everything that happened to me that summer happened because of Winn-Dixie.**" Think about your answer to question 1 at the beginning of the last chapter, and about what you have read in Chapters Six to Ten. Is Opal's claim accurate? Give two reasons for your answer.

_____

_____

_____

2. How do thunderstorms make you feel? What do you do when there is a particularly bad one? Explain in detail.

_____

_____

Vocabulary

VERBS are words that show actions (for example: He <u>ran</u> to school.) or states of being (for example: He <u>is</u> happy.). Use each of the following VERBS correctly in a sentence.

1. **whining** _____

2. **whimpering** _____

3. **trembling** _____

4. **shaking** _____

5. **flew** _____

6. **panting** _____

7. **screamed** _____

8. **loved** _____

NAME: _____

Chapter Eleven

Part A

1. **Complete the paragraph by filling in each black with the correct word from the chapter.**

One night, there was a terrible _____ , and it scared _____
                                                  a   b

a lot. He ran all over Opal's bedroom, butting his head against the bedroom

_____ . When Opal called him, he didn't pay any_____
        c   d

to her. Winn-Dixie was_____ and _____ . Then the
                                e   f

_____ woke up and asked what was going on. Winn-Dixie ran at him
        g

like a _____ and knocked him down. The preacher said that
              h

Winn-Dixie had a pathological _____ . When the _____
                                    i   j

ended, Opal loved the preacher very much, because he tried to keep Winn-Dixie

_____ .
        k

2. Circle **T** if the statement is TRUE or **F** if it is FALSE.

T F   **a)** Winn-Dixie ran and played during the thunderstorm.
              One crack of thunder was so loud it shook the whole trailer.

T F   **b)** Eventually, Opal just let Winn-Dixie run around because his fear
              was too great.

T F   **c)** When the storm ended, Winn-Dixie seemed surprised that Opal
              and the preacher were out of bed.

T F   **d)** The preacher said that they would ignore Winn-Dixie every time
              there was a thunderstorm.

T F   **e)** The preacher forgave Winn-Dixie for being afraid, and for waking
              them up. He showed this by putting his arm around Winn-Dixie
              to keep him safe.

Chapter Eleven

Part B

Answer the questions in complete sentences.

1. This is a very important chapter because Opal learns that her father truly wants to keep Winn-Dixie safe, and with them. What is the most important thing that he does to show this?

   _____

   _____

2. What can we infer about Opal eventually not trying to stop Winn-Dixie from running around the trailer? What has she learned?

   _____

   _____

3. When the preacher puts his arm around Winn-Dixie, he does it to make him feel safe, and to make sure he doesn't run away. Explain why this would be a very important gesture to Opal.

   _____

   _____

   _____

4. Why does Opal feel so much love for her father at that moment? Give at least two reasons for your opinion.

   _____

   _____

Journal Activity

In this chapter we see how the relationship between Opal and her father is deepening, and in doing so, we learn more about the preacher. Pretend you are Opal. Write down five to ten things you know about the preacher.

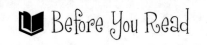

NAME: _____

Chapters Twelve to Fourteen

Answer the questions in complete sentences.

1. In many of the books we read, or movies we see, there are strange, unexplained, magical moments when something wonderful happens. Think of a time in a book or a movie that something wonderful or magical happened, and describe it here.

_____

_____

_____

2. Have you ever known a person who always said, "If you do that, I'll tell on you"? How did it make you feel? What did you do? Give details.

_____

_____

Vocabulary

To make their writing more interesting, and to give us clues about how a character is feeling, authors use many different words to take the place of the word "said". Here are some examples from the next few chapters.

shouted   told   asked   hollered   whispered

Use each of these "said" words in its own sentence, making sure to use quotation marks ("   ") correctly.

_____

_____

_____

_____

_____

Chapters Twelve to Fourteen

Part A

Put a check mark next to the answer that is most correct.

1. **Opal sees Otis playing his guitar for the animals, smiling, with his eyes closed. How did his music affect the animals in the pet shop, all of whom were out of their cages?**

   ○ **A** They made loud noises, and ran every which way they could.
   ○ **B** They all sat perfectly still, like stone statues, listening.
   ○ **C** They had all fallen asleep.

2. **What broke the spell of the music over the animals?**

   ○ **A** Gertrude croaked, "Dog!", and landed on Winn-Dixie's head, causing Otis to stop and look up.
   ○ **B** Otis finished the song he was playing, and took a break from singing.
   ○ **C** Winn-Dixie barked at the animals and scared them.

3. **What secret does Opal learn about Otis that makes her think her dad wouldn't be happy about her working there if he knew it?**

   ○ **A** Otis is poor.
   ○ **B** Otis has been in jail.
   ○ **C** Otis does not attend church.

4. **Which two boys bother Opal as she goes to Gloria Dump's house each day, making her feel all worn out?**

   ○ **A** Otis and the preacher
   ○ **B** Robbie and Bradley
   ○ **C** Dunlap and Stevie Dewberry

5. **What does Gloria Dump have hanging from a tree to keep away all the ghosts of the things she has done wrong?**

   ○ **A** letters and notes
   ○ **B** empty glass bottles
   ○ **C** old photographs

NAME: _____

Chapters Twelve to Fourteen

Part B

Answer the questions in complete sentences.

1. How would you explain Otis' ability to play music that keeps the animals silent and still. Is it magic? Explain your opinion.

_____

_____

2. What words or reactions support the idea that even though Gloria Dump's eyes **"ain't too good at all"**, she is better able to understand, to **"see"**, what people are really like? Find proof in the story.

_____

_____

3. The glass bottles in Gloria Dump's tree represent all the things she has done wrong. Their description puts a clear image, or picture, in our minds. Which words or phrases does Kate DiCamillo use to help create this image for you?

_____

_____

4. Gloria Dump tells Opal to judge people by what they are doing now, and not by what they have done in the past. For example, she tells Opal to judge Otis by his kindness to animals and by the pretty music he plays, and not by the fact that he went to jail. Do you think that this is good advice?

_____

_____

Journal Activity

Gloria Dump says that each of us must learn what is the most important to us, by ourselves. If you had to write about what was most important to you, what would it be? Tell about what is most important to you.

Chapters Fifteen to Seventeen

Answer the questions in complete sentences.

1. What is your favorite kind of candy? Why do you like it? How does it make you feel when you are eating it? Explain.

_____

2. Think of an elderly relative you know, perhaps even someone who lives with your family, or of an elderly person on your street or in your building. The elderly have special needs because of their age, because they aren't able to do all of the things that they once could. List two or three things that you could do to help an elderly person, and explain why you would do each of these things.

_____

_____

Vocabulary

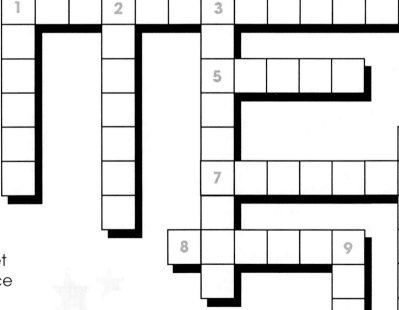

Down

1. He ran _____ the table.
2. She is sad; we must _____ her.
3. A weed with a yellow flower
4. Your mom or dad's father
6. The opposite of forget
9. The opposite of peace

Across

1. This cools air inside when it is hot outside.
5. A long chapter book
7. A candy to suck on for a sore throat
8. Another word for sadness

Word List:

around	lozenge	war
airconditioning	remember	comfort
grandfather	novel	sorrow
dandelion		

NAME: _____

Chapters Fifteen to Seventeen

Part A

1. **Which answer best describes...**

a) what happens occasionally to Miss Franny?

- ○ **A** She has a small fit.
- ○ **B** She falls asleep.
- ○ **C** She can't see very well.

b) how Winn-Dixie helps Miss Franny when she has a fit?

- ○ **A** He smiles at her.
- ○ **B** He becomes mean.
- ○ **C** He protects her and licks her hand.

c) the reason for the American Civil War?

- ○ **A** a misunderstanding
- ○ **B** a war over slavery
- ○ **C** wanting more land

d) the situation Littmus W. Block was in after the Civil War?

- ○ **A** He was dead.
- ○ **B** He was an orphan.
- ○ **C** He was promoted.

e) what Littmus did after the war?

- ○ **A** He made candles.
- ○ **B** He went to Canada.
- ○ **C** He invented a candy.

f) what a Littmus Lozenge tastes like?

- ○ **A** sadness
- ○ **B** joy
- ○ **C** forgetfulness

2. **Circle T if the statement is TRUE or F if it is FALSE.**

T F **a)** A Littmus Lozenge tastes both sad and sweet.

T F **b)** Opal was sad about leaving her old town, Whatley, and all her friends behind when she moved.

T F **c)** Miss Franny only had three candies to share.

T F **d)** Miss Franny suggested Opal read <u>Gone With the Wind</u> to the preacher.

T F **e)** Pinched-faced Amanda Wilkinson is sad because she misses Carson.

After You Read

Chapters Fifteen to Seventeen

Part B

Answer the questions in complete sentences.

1. Retell the sad story of Littmus and what he found when he returned from the Civil War. Be sure to tell why he decided to create a new kind of candy.

    _____

    _____

    _____

2. How is Littmus' story similar to both Opal and Miss Franny's lives? Compare the three characters by listing the similarities.

    _____

    _____

    _____

3. After Amanda says she misses Carson, Miss Franny says, **"It is a sorrow-filled world"**. What can you infer about Amanda from this statement?

    _____

    _____

4. In your opinion, why does Opal want a Littmus Lozenge for all the people in her life? Why does she want to share them?

    _____

    _____

Journal Activity

If you could invent a special candy, what affect would it have on the people that tasted it? Why would you want them to feel this way? What would your candy taste like? How would you put that feeling into the candy?

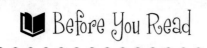 **Before You Read**

NAME: _____

Chapters Eighteen to Twenty

Answer the questions in complete sentences.

1. The last chapter ends with Opal thinking about Amanda Wilkinson, and asking the question **"Who was Carson?"** Predict who Carson might have been, and why Amanda misses him.

   _____

   _____

2. It seems that many of the characters in the novel feel lonely. When have you felt lonely before? Think of a time you were lonely, and tell about it.

   _____

   _____

Vocabulary

Here are some words from the next few chapters. Using a straight line, match each word on the left to its definition on the right. If you're not sure about what they mean, look them up in the dictionary. When you have finished, circle your favorite two words and use them in complete sentences on the lines provided.

#	Word		Definition	
1	sorrowful		being lazy; not doing anything	A
2	melancholy		having a discussion	B
3	idle		full of sadness	C
4	conversation		important idea in a book, a song, etc.	D
5	theme		a feeling of sadness	E

_____

_____

Chapters Eighteen to Twenty

Part A

1. **Which character's name is the answer to each question below?
Write the correct name in the box beside the question.**

Gloria Dump   Carson   the preacher   Otis   Sweetie Pie

a) Which character said the Littmus Lozenge tasted like melancholy, and reminded him of his wife?

b) Which character does Amanda miss very much, because he drowned when he was only five years old?

c) Which character cried when he tasted the Littmus Lozenge, because it tasted like being in jail?

d) Which character said, **"the whole world has an aching heart"**, and that a Littmus Lozenge tasted like people leaving?

e) Which character spit out the Littmus Lozenge because it tasted, to her, like not having a dog as a pet?

2. **Circle T if the statement is TRUE or F if it is FALSE.**

T F **a)** Otis went to jail because he hit a policeman who was trying to stop him from playing his guitar in the street.

T F **b)** Gloria Dump made Opal promise to invite the Dewberry boys to their party.

T F **c)** Sweetie Pie Thomas has a dog as a pet.

T F **d)** Otis refused to come to the party.

T F **e)** Opal felt sad for Amanda's tragic loss.

NAME: _____

Chapters Eighteen to Twenty

Part B

1. **Complete the chart to tell what you know about the following characters.**

Character's Name	How they reacted when they ate the Littmus Lozenge?	What does this tell us about their personality or their feelings?
A Gloria Dump		
B the preacher		
C Otis		
D Sweetie Pie		

Answer the questions in complete sentences.

2. Explain what Gloria Dump means when she says, **"the whole world has an aching heart"**. Give two examples from the story that prove that she is correct.

_____

_____

_____

3. In your opinion, why does Opal decide that they need to have a party?

_____

_____

Journal Activity

If you were planning a special party, what would be the reason for holding it? Who would you invite? What special activities would you have? What kind of food would you serve? Plan your special party.

Chapters Twenty-One to Twenty-Three

Answer the questions in complete sentences.

1. Tell about a party that you once attended. Who was it for, and what was the occasion? Did you enjoy yourself? Describe the party.

_____

_____

2. Tell about a special event, a field trip, a sporting event, or another occasion you were supposed to have that was spoiled by bad weather. Describe what happened, and how it made you feel.

_____

Vocabulary

Complete the two charts by filling in the blank boxes.

	Word from story	Base Word (root word)	Ending
1.	convinced	convince	-ed
A	wagging		-ing
B	desperately	desperate	
C	smiling		-ing

	Compound word from story	Two words that make up that word	
2.	somebody	some	body
A	flashlight		
B	downpour		
C	grapefruit		

NAME: _____

Chapters Twenty-One to Twenty-Three

Part A

1. **Which answer best describes...**

a) Otis?
- ○ **A** shy
- ○ **B** loud and talkative
- ○ **C** confident

b) the sandwiches they ate?
- ○ **A** ham and cheese
- ○ **B** salmon
- ○ **C** egg salad

c) how Opal felt when she saw Amanda?
- ○ **A** upset
- ○ **B** very glad
- ○ **C** shy

d) the weather at the party?
- ○ **A** clear and sunny
- ○ **B** rain and thunder
- ○ **C** snowy and cold

2. **Put a check mark next to the answer that is most correct.**

a) Why did Opal stand close to Amanda Wilkinson and why was she extra nice to her?
- ○ **A** She was worried Amanda would be mean to someone.
- ○ **B** Amanda asked her to stand close by.
- ○ **C** Opal felt very sorry for Amanda's loss, and wanted to show her through her actions, not her words.

b) As everyone ran inside, to get out of the rain and the thunder, what did Opal realize she had forgotten?
- ○ **A** She forgot to bring in the pickle jar.
- ○ **B** She forgot to protect Winn-Dixie from the thunder.
- ○ **C** She forgot to help Gloria Dump with the sandwiches.

c) When Opal decides to go look for Winn-Dixie, what does Gloria Dump tell her?
- ○ **A** "You can only love what you got while you got it."
- ○ **B** "There ain't no way you can hold onto something that wants to go."
- ○ **C** All of the above.

Chapters Twenty-One to Twenty-Three

Part B

Answer the questions in complete sentences.

1. Look at Gloria Dump's words in question 2 c) of the previous page. We know she is talking about Winn-Dixie here, but how might her words also be about Opal's mother? Explain your thoughts.

   _____

   _____

2. What can we infer about Opal from her reaction to forgetting about Winn-Dixie? Why did she feel like crying?

   _____

   _____

3. Evaluate Opal as a pet owner. Has she done a good job of caring for Winn-Dixie? Support your opinions with proof from the story.

   _____

   _____

4. Think about all of the people invited to Opal and Gloria Dump's garden party. What do they all have in common? Compare three of the guests.

   _____

   _____

   _____

Journal Activity

Pretend you are Opal, just at the moment that she realizes that Winn-Dixie is missing. How would you feel? Why would you feel this way? Write Opal's journal entry showing her feelings at this moment.

 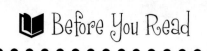
Chapters Twenty-Four to Twenty-Six

Answer the questions in complete sentences.

1. Before you begin the final chapters, think about Gloria Dump's words again: **"There ain't no way you can hold onto something that wants to go."** Do you think Opal would have felt much better throughout the novel if she had heard this advice early on? Explain your answer.

   _____

2. Think about someone in your family, maybe your mom or dad, maybe a brother or a sister, or maybe another relative. Write down five things that make that family member special to you.

   _____

   _____

3. Predict how Winn-Dixie's disappearance and Gloria's advice will affect Opal and her relationship with her father.

   _____

Vocabulary

Using a dictionary, find the <u>meaning</u> of each of the following words.
In the boxes, write each word's <u>part of speech</u> (noun, verb, adjective, etc.).
You may illustrate your definitions if you wish.

1	downtown		_____
2	taillight		_____
3	memorize		_____
4	drizzle		_____
5	realize		_____

Chapters Twenty-Four to Twenty-Six

Part A

1. **Number the events from ❶ to ❺ in the order they occurred in the chapters.**

_____ **a)** When Opal and her father returned to Gloria Dump's house they were surprised to find that Winn-Dixie had been there all along, hiding and sleeping under Gloria's chair.

_____ **b)** The preacher admits, sadly, that he doesn't think Opal's mom will ever come back.

_____ **c)** Opal and the preacher go out into the rain to look for Winn-Dixie.

_____ **d)** The rain and thunder came, forcing everyone inside for the party.

_____ **e)** The preacher cries when he thinks about how he failed at keeping Opal's mom in their home, and at how upset he is about losing Winn-Dixie. Opal comforts him by hugging him.

2. **Circle T if the statement is TRUE or F if it is FALSE.**

T   F   **a)** Gloria Dump convinces Dunlap and Stevie that she really isn't a witch.

T   F   **b)** Winn-Dixie's sneeze let everyone know that he hadn't run out of the house and yard.

T   F   **c)** Winn-Dixie looked like a ghost because he was covered in dust.

T   F   **d)** Opal learns that while she misses her mom, she must move on and appreciate those around her, in the present.

T   F   **e)** Winn-Dixie was sleeping under Gloria Dump's chair because he was worn out from the thunderstorm.

NAME: _____

Chapters Twenty-Four to Twenty-Six

Part B

Answer the questions in complete sentences.

1. What does Opal learn about her father in these chapters? How did she feel when he said that her mother wasn't coming back, and then began to cry? Do you think it changes the way she looks at him?

   _____

   _____

2. What can we infer about Opal from her decision to think about her mom from time to time, but not as much as she had? Why has she had this change of heart?

   _____

   _____

3. Why was it better that Winn-Dixie was in Gloria Dump's house all along, and not lost in the streets? How did you feel when you learned that Winn-Dixie wasn't lost? Explain.

   _____

   _____

4. Give your opinion about the end of the novel, when everyone is sitting around singing and enjoying being together. Do you think it was a good way to end the book? Explain your answer.

   _____

   _____

Journal Activity

Was **Because of Winn-Dixie** a realistic story? Write a journal entry about why you think this was, or was not, a realistic story. Give proof from the novel in your answer.

Chapters 1 to 5

In the early chapters of the novel, we are introduced to Opal and her father, and the relationship they have. Into this family comes Winn-Dixie, and things begin to change for Opal. Pretend you are Opal, and <u>write a diary</u> of the first few days that you have Winn-Dixie, from the first time you see him in the grocery store, to the time he catches the mouse in the Open Arms Baptist Church.

For each diary entry, consider:

- what your family situation is, and your relationship with the preacher;
- what events happen because of Winn-Dixie;
- how your relationship with the preacher begins to change;
- how Winn-Dixie begins to change both yourself and the preacher.

📓 WriTinG Task #2

Chapters 6, 7, 15, 16 and 17

Opal's first friend in Naomi is Miss Franny Block, the librarian at the Herman W. Block Memorial Library. Think about Miss Franny, and the stories she tells, and pretend you are writing a chapter in a <u>nonfiction tour book</u> about the famous people and history of Naomi, Florida.
Write the chapter about Miss Franny, her library, and her family's history.
Include as many details from the novel as you can.

For example, you may wish to begin in this way:

One of Naomi's oldest living residents is Miss Franny Block, the librarian at the Herman W. Block Memorial Library, and heiress to the Block family fortune.

Writing Task #3

Chapters 9, 10, 13, 14, 18 and 20

One of the most important people that Opal meets that summer in Naomi,
is Gloria Dump. Opal comes to enjoy her peanut butter sandwiches, her company, and,
most importantly, to rely on her as a friend with whom she can share her thoughts and
feelings, and as a friend who gives valuable advice about life and relationships.

The preacher told Opal ten things about her mother, and Opal made up a list of ten things
she knew about Winn-Dixie. Both lists were special because they allowed Opal
to remember important things about those she loved.

> **Pretend you are Opal.**
> **Write a list of <u>Ten Things I Know about Gloria Dump</u>.**
>
> Which things will you include? What is most important to you?
> Think about what you know about Gloria Dump,
> and why she is important to you.

 # Writing Task #4

Chapters 8, 12 and 19

> Pretend you are a newspaper reporter given the job of writing about Otis.
> Write **two articles** about him, one based on **facts**,
> and one based on **your opinions**.

Consider these things as you write:

• <u>**Your first article**</u> should report on the time when Otis was arrested
after he knocked out the policeman. Write only about the facts of that event,
without any opinions of your own. What happened? Where did it happen?
What were the consequences of Otis' actions?

• <u>**Your second article**</u> is a follow-up report, checking in on Otis.
For this article interview India Opal Buloni, a young girl who works with Otis at
Gertrude's Pets, and report on the magical event you witness one morning while
looking in the pet shop's window. How has your perception of Otis changed?
How do you feel about him now? Give your opinions, supported by facts from the story.

Chapter 20

**Opal and Gloria Dump are planning a garden party,
and they have asked you to <u>design the invitation</u>.
What will the invitation say? Time? Place? Treats and food?
What design will you have on the invitation? Think about these things,
and then create your invitation.**

When writing your invitation, think about:

- What size will it be?
- What kind of lettering will you use?
- Will it be hand written, or typed on the computer?
- Which colors will you use? • What will your envelope look like?
- To whom will you address the card and envelope?

Chapters 23 to 26

Pretend you are Opal. During the thunderstorm, when you think you have lost Winn-Dixie, just like you lost your mother, you finally confront the preacher about the time your mother went away, and ask if he thinks she'll ever come back. The preacher's reaction surprises you, and you suddenly realize that Gloria Dump was right when she said,
"You can only love what you got while you got it."

As Opal, write her <u>final diary entry</u> for that first summer in Naomi. Think about all that has happened, the new friends you have made, and how they each have helped you mature and grow. Think about Winn-Dixie, and how he has helped you, too. And finally, think about the preacher, and what you have learned about your mother. How has your relationship with the preacher changed? Why are you now closer to him than you have ever been before? Why do you believe that your heart is now full?

Include details from the story to support your ideas.

After You Read 📖

Word Search

Find all of the words in the word search. Words may be horizontal, vertical, or diagonal. A few may even be backwards. Look carefully!

jungle	knuckle	apologize	lizard
melancholy	pathological	slither	weight
wrappers	neighborhood	lozenge	hollered
trustworthy	whistling	whimpering	memorize
department	vegetables	thunderstorm	surprise
squawked	peculiar	everybody	wagging
orphan	swollen	echoed	tongue

g	f	e	d	c	b	a	o	p	e	c	h	o	e	d	m	x	w
a	c	b	d	o	p	e	t	h	m	e	m	o	r	i	z	e	r
b	o	q	r	s	l	m	p	e	c	u	l	i	a	r	l	n	a
c	s	t	u	o	q	e	v	e	r	y	b	o	d	y	d	o	p
d	w	h	i	s	t	l	i	n	g	a	c	e	g	o	b	c	p
e	o	i	j	k	l	a	t	u	a	p	o	l	o	g	i	z	e
f	l	l	k	o	k	n	u	c	k	l	e	q	a	b	c	d	r
t	l	o	p	q	r	c	m	v	e	g	e	t	a	b	l	e	s
u	e	w	e	i	g	h	t	s	u	r	p	r	i	s	e	a	i
r	n	s	o	m	r	o	t	s	r	e	d	n	u	h	t	n	n
e	g	n	e	z	o	l	i	j	k	l	m	n	c	o	n	u	g
q	u	a	v	e	g	y	l	m	n	q	o	e	h	l	e	b	p
a	c	w	a	g	g	i	n	g	m	i	m	i	o	l	m	c	a
m	b	d	o	t	w	u	z	x	t	a	b	g	q	e	t	d	t
m	s	m	n	a	l	i	z	a	r	d	l	h	u	r	r	e	h
s	m	q	b	d	b	m	a	s	o	x	y	b	e	e	a	d	o
l	s	j	u	n	g	l	e	a	r	c	d	o	s	d	p	q	l
i	t	u	v	a	o	m	e	e	p	g	t	r	g	m	e	u	o
t	r	u	s	t	w	o	r	t	h	y	o	h	g	m	d	r	g
h	i	j	l	e	f	k	l	l	a	y	n	o	o	t	p	m	i
e	m	l	m	g	j	k	e	l	n	v	g	o	n	h	e	l	c
r	o	m	c	d	h	s	q	d	m	v	u	d	a	f	n	m	a
c	w	h	i	m	p	e	r	i	n	g	e	n	q	m	t	m	l

Because of Winn-Dixie CC2301

Comprehension Quiz

Answer the questions in complete sentences.

1. Where does Opal first see Winn-Dixie? What is he doing, and what does she do to save him?

_____

_____

2. What important things does Opal learn about her mother when she asks the preacher to tell her ten things about her?

_____

_____

3. What does Opal think of the Dewberry boys, Stevie and Dunlap? How does her opinion of them slowly change throughout the novel?

_____

_____

4. At first, Opal thinks that Amanda Wilkinson is pinch-faced and unfriendly. How does her opinion of Amanda change, and why?

_____

_____

5. Why does the story of Amanda's brother Carson affect Opal so much? How is Amanda's loss like the situation with Opal's mother?

_____

_____

6. How does Gertrude the parrot help Opal get a job in Gertrude's Pet Shop? How does she help Otis decide to hire Opal?

_____

_____

SUBTOTAL: /12

NAME: _____

Comprehension Quiz

7. What two tastes does a Littmus Lozenge have? Why does every character have a similar reaction when they taste the candy?

_____

_____

(2)

8. Opal is frantic when she can't find Winn-Dixie during the thunderstorm, and she feels that he is gone because she forgot to hold onto him and protect him. How is this like her feelings about herself, the preacher, and her mother?

_____

_____

(2)

9. At first, the preacher seemed kind of cool to the idea of keeping Winn-Dixie as a pet. How does he change by the end of the novel?

_____

_____

(2)

10. Why does Gloria Dump wish Opal good luck as Opal goes out to look for Winn-Dixie?

_____

_____

(2)

11. Why is it important for the novel that Dunlap, and later Amanda, are the ones who go out and bring Opal back into the party? How have things changed for them all?

_____

_____

(2)

12. As everyone sings for Winn-Dixie at the end of the novel, and Opal sucks on a Littmus Lozenge, why is it so important for her to remember who is there, and what they are singing?

_____

_____

(2)

SUBTOTAL: /12

1. Answers will vary

2. He was hesitating, not sure if he wanted to answer

3. She could recognize and hold on tight to her if she returned

4. Answers will vary

15

1. ⊘ B

2. ⊘ A

3. ⊘ C

4. ⊘ B

14

1. Answers will vary

2. Answers will vary

1. handsome

2. ten

3. shiny, soft

4. funny

13

1. Answers will vary

2. Kind, helpful to those who need it

3. Answers will vary / She is usually alone

4. Keeps things to himself, quiet and private when he feels uncomfortable

5. Causes preacher to open up, come out of his shell

12

1.
a) ⊘ B   b) ⊘ C
c) ⊘ C   d) ⊘ A
e) ⊘ B   f) ⊘ C

2.
a) Ⓣ
b) Ⓕ
c) Ⓣ
d) Ⓣ
e) Ⓣ

11

1. Answers will vary

2. Answers will vary

a) a minister
b) to have one's attention diverted

2. yelled

3. tangled

1. Looks at his feet, stumbles over his words

2. Answers will vary

3. Has to trust her heart to help her know a person; Asks her to tell her everything about herself

4. Tells about new friends and job; Answers will vary

1.
a) 3
b) 1
c) 5
d) 2
e) 4

2.
a) ○ B b) ✓ C
c) ✓ A d) ○ C

---

1. Answers will vary; gives her confidence

2. Answers will vary

Vocabulary

1. (n.) small rodent kept as a pet
2. (adj.) very angry
3. (n.) a part of something
4. (adj.) deserving of trust
5. (adj.) grown over with weeds
6. (adj.) wrinkled

---

1. She liked Miss Franny's stories

2. He was a very rich man

3. Both are lonely, have lost someone dear to them: Miss Franny - her friends; Opal - her mother

4. Answers will vary

5. Answers will vary

1.
a) ✓ A b) ○ C
c) ○ B d) ✓ C
e) ✓ A f) ○ B

2.
a) ⊤
b) ⊤
c) ⧸F
d) ⊤
e) ⧸F

---

1. Answers will vary

2. Answers will vary

Vocabulary

Across:
1. mosquitoes
2. librarian
3. bear
4. stories
5. friend

Down:
1. ma'am
2. library
6. Amanda
7. reader
8. mood

1. Answers will vary

2. Her experiences (bottles, etc.) have taught her that it's a person's actions that count the most, not what others say about you

3. Possible answers: hanging, bottles, clanking, spooky kind of noise, hair rose up a little, growled, ghosts

4. Answers will vary

28

1. B

2. A

3. B

4. C

5. B

27

1. Answers will vary

2. Answers will vary

Vocabulary

Sentences will vary

26

1. Puts his arm around him to keep him safe

2. She is smart enough to realize that it's best to let him go until he calms down

3. It means he doesn't want to lose him; might suggest something he didn't do with her mother

4. Answers will vary; He loves Winn-Dixie; he knows that Winn-Dixie is important to Opal

25

1.
a) thunderstorm
b) Winn-Dixie
c) door
d) attention
e) crying
f) shaking
g) preacher
h) bowling ball
i) fear
j) storm
k) safe

2.
a) F
b) T
c) F
d) T
e) F

24

1. Answers will vary

2. Answers will vary

Vocabulary

Sentences will vary

23

1.

a) Felt like people leaving; lonely

b) Melancholy; lonely, misses his wife

c) Felt like being in jail; lonely

d) Felt like not having a dog; wants a dog

2.

Everyone feels sadness; Amanda's heart aches for her brother; Opal's aches for her mother

3.

Answers will vary

(34)

1.

a) the preacher

b) Carson

c) Otis

d) Gloria Dump

e) Sweetie Pie

2.

a) T

b) T

c) F

d) F

e) T

(33)

1.

Answers will vary

2.

Answers will vary

1	C
2	E
3	A
4	B
5	D

(32)

1.

Answers will vary; include the facts about his family, his feelings of sorrow, etc.

2.

All have suffered a loss, feel sadness, longing, sense of abandonment, are eager to share with others

3.

Has known sorrow in her life

4.

Answers will vary

(31)

1.

a) A

b) C

c) B

d) B

e) C

f) A

2.

a) T

b) T

c) F

d) F

e) T

(30)

1.

Answers will vary

2.

Answers will vary

Down:
1. around
2. comfort
3. dandelion
4. grandfather
6. remember
5. war

Across:
1. air conditioning
2. novel
3. lozenge
4. sorrow

(29)

1.
He is very sad about losing his wife, tried to keep her; She tried to comfort him, loves him even more

2.
Has learned to live in the present, love those around her

3.
Answers will vary

4.
Answers will vary

1.
a) 5
b) 3
c) 2
d) 1
e) 4

2.
a) T
b) T
c) T
d) T
e) T

1.
Answers will vary; Yes, it would have helped her cope better

2.
Answers will vary

3.
Answers will vary

Vocabulary
1. (n.) business part of a city or town
2. (n.) rear light on a car
3. (v.) commit to memory
4. (n.) light rain with small raindrops
5. (v.) be aware of/ recognize something

1.
Since Opal's mother wanted to go, there was nothing anyone could've done to stop her. Answers will vary.

2.
Very responsible, feels she let him down when he needed her most; felt like crying because she thought she had failed, let him get away, just like her mother

3.
Answers will vary

4.
Possible answers: all are lonely, have suffered a loss, need friends

---

1.
a) ⊙ A   b) ⊙ C
c) ⊙ B   d) ⊙ B

2.
a) ⊙ C
b) ⊙ B
c) ⊙ C

1.
Answers will vary

2.
Answers will vary

Vocabulary

1.
A wag
B -ly
C smile

2.
A flash/light
B down/pour
C grape/fruit

Because of Winn-Dixie CC2301

Word Search Answers

7. Sweet, sad; all have suffered a loss or similar loneliness

8. Accuses preacher of not holding onto her mother, he tells her he tried, but failed. Feels she wasn't responsible enough to remember his fear, so she lost him too.

9. Grows to love Winn-Dixie as much as Opal does; he is upset, frantic to find him

10. Possible answers: Knows how important Winn-Dixie is to her; doesn't want her to suffer another loss, etc.

11. They have become her real friends; they want her around, will look for her to bring her where it is warm and dry; don't want her to miss the singing

12. Possible answers: So she won't ever forget this happiest of moments; has found a place where she belongs, wants to be, and where others want her

1. In the produce section of the Winn-Dixie grocery store; running around; claims he is hers

2. Possible answers: couldn't cook, had green thumb, didn't like being a preacher's wife, drank, etc.

3. Are mean, unfriendly; Gloria Dump encourages her to be friendly; the boys gradually become friendly, especially Dunlap

4. As she learns about Carson, she empathizes with Amanda, understands her behavior

5. Opal has suffered the loss of her mother, so she knows how sad Amanda must feel

6. Gertrude lands on Winn-Dixie's head - shows that she likes him; this convinces Otis - the dog will likely be around a lot.

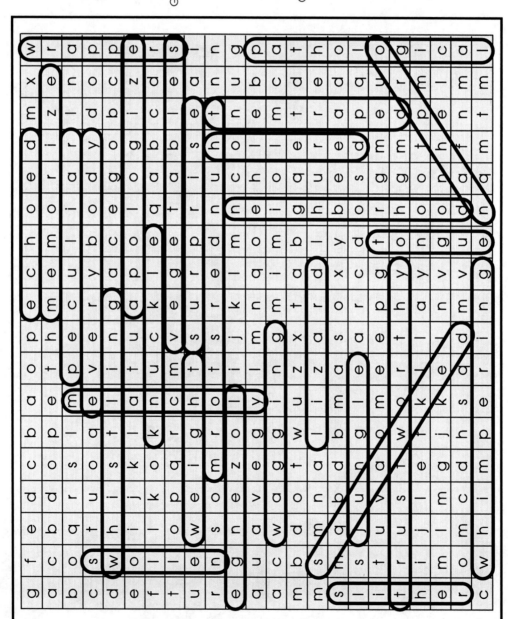

Because of Winn-Dixie CC2301